BENI FUJIWARA, A HIGH SCHOOL GIRL WHO WANTED TO DIE TO GET BACK AT HER ARROGANT FATHER, WAS UNEXPECTEDLY RESCUED WHEN SHE FELL OFF A BUILDING ONE DAY. HER SAVIOR? A NINJA NAMED KAGETORA, WHO HAPPENED TO FALL OUT OF THE SKY AT THE RIGHT MOMENT. KAGETORA CALLS BENI "BENI HIME," AND HE DEVOTES HIMSELF TO PROTECTING HER LIFE AT ANY COST...BECAUSE HE'D MISTAKEN HER FOR HER OWN ANCESTOR, WHO LOOKED EXACTLY LIKE HER. YES, KAGETORA WAS A NINJA WHO'D TRAVELED THROUGH TIME FROM THE PAST! KAGETORA BELIEVES THAT THE MODERN WORLD, SO DIFFERENT FROM HIS OWN, IS NOTHING BUT AN ILLUSION. AS TIME PASSES, BENI GRADUALLY BECOMES FOND OF KAGETORA AS HE REPEATEDLY SAVES HER FROM DANGER AND PLEDGES HIS ETERNAL LOYALTY. SHE TRIES TO PRETEND TO BE BENI HIME FOR HIM, AND THEY SLOWLY BECOME CLOSER AND CLOSER. BUT WHEN THE PAIR UNEXPECTEDLY TRAVELS BACK TO KAGETORA'S TIME, HE RUNS INTO THE REAL BENI HIME AND REALIZES THAT THE TWO WOMEN ARE NOT THE SAME PERSON. AFTER BENI HIME TELLS KAGETORA THAT SHE WANTS TO LIVE AS A NORMAL VILLAGER, HE LOSES HIS PURPOSE IN LIFE. A FELLOW NINJA, HITAKI, BRANDS HIM A TRAITOR AND TRIES TO KILL HIM, SO KAGETORA DECIDES TO RETURN TO THE PRESENT WITH BENI AND LIVE WITH HER, BUT...

Summary & Character Introduction

BENI FUJIWARA
A HIGH SCHOOL GIRL WHO STARTS TO LIKE KAGETORA (?!).

BENI'S FATHER
A COLD MAN, UNINTERESTED IN HIS DAUGHTER.

HITAKI
KAGETORA'S NINJA FRIEND. HE TRIES TO TAKE KAGETORA'S LIFE.

KUROKI
BENI'S FATHER'S PET DOG.

TAKEZAKI
BENI'S FATHER'S SECRETARY.

BENI HIME
BENI'S ANCESTOR AND KAGETORA'S FORMER MASTER.

KAGETORA
A NINJA WHO CAME FROM THE PAST.

Chapter 5

Shinobi Life

You whisper

You whisper

EVERYONE, THIS IS OUR NEW STUDENT, KAGETORA FUJIWARA-KUN.

...YOU REALLY HAVE NO IDEA HOW CONSPICUOUS YOU ARE, DO YOU?

YOU ALWAYS FOLLOW ME AROUND AND SAY YOU'RE GOING TO PROTECT ME, BUT...

BUT WHY?!

ON TOP OF THAT, EVERYBODY WEARS A UNIFORM AT SCHOOL, SO...

What's that?

SNEAKING AROUND LIKE THAT ATTRACTS **MORE** ATTENTION, NOT LESS!

Whoa...!

...SOMEONE WEARING REGULAR CLOTHES REALLY STANDS OUT.

YOU... WISH ME TO ATTEND THE SAME SCHOOL AS YOU, BENI-SAMA?

THE BEST PLACE TO HIDE A TREE IS IN THE WOODS.

IF YOU DON'T WANT TO DRAW ATTENTION, IT'S BEST TO DO WHAT EVERYONE ELSE IS DOING!

GET IT?

JUST KEEP YOUR EYES OPEN AND COPY WHAT YOU SEE PEOPLE DOING.

TRY AND GET USED TO SCHOOL QUICKLY, OKAY?

Y-YES, MA'AM.

YOU'RE THE GUY WHO KEPT TAGGING ALONG TO SCHOOL WITH FUJIWARA-SAN, RIGHT?

...the school out before transferring here?

Were you just checking...

WOW, THE GIRLS ARE HITTING ON HIM ALREADY!

HEY, KAGE-TORA-KUN.

HE SAID HE UNDER-STANDS, BUT... I'M WORRIED. HE DOESN'T KNOW ANYTHING ABOUT NORMAL LIFE.

HE'S A NINJA, AFTER ALL....

OH! ARE YOU GUYS...

WHY IS YOUR LAST NAME FUJIWARA TOO?

I'M A LITTLE DIS-APPOINTED, BUT...

IT'S TRUE THAT YOU CAN NEVER TELL WHAT HE'S THINKING...

...BUT WE'RE IN THE SAME CLASS, THAT'S ALL.

I THINK THAT WAS THE FIRST TIME...

...THAT I EVEN REALLY TALKED TO HIM.

WHAT EXACTLY DO YOU WANT ME TO BE CAREFUL OF...?

RIGHT, KUROKI?

SO EVEN IF YOU TELL ME TO BE CAUTIOUS, THERE ISN'T ANYTHING I CAN DO ABOUT IT.

Eek!

THAT'S SIMPLE.

JUST AVOID CONVERSING WITH HIM.

shff...

YOU KNOW, I...

I...

I...ALWAYS THOUGHT THAT I LIKED KAGETORA TOO MUCH...

...AND I BELIEVED THAT HIS FEELINGS WERE FOR BENI HIME, NOT ME.

BUT MY FEELINGS FOR HIM JUST KEPT GROWING...

AND IT'S ME HE'S SEEING RIGHT NOW.

I FEEL THE SAME--

Ruff!

THERE YOU ARE, KUROKI.

Rurrr...

Recently I discovered that when cats start twisting and turning because they don't want to be held, they also spin their tails around like cheetahs.

Whoa!

Cheetahs spin their tails like that when they're running and want to change direction. They really are all part of the same cat family.

I'll be waiting for your comments! ✿

TOKYOPOP, Inc.
5900 Wilshire Blvd.
Suite # 2000
Los Angeles, CA 90036

Attn: Shinobi Life Editor

And we meet again! Hello, this is Conami! Oh, but maybe there are some people who I haven't met yet...? It's nice to meet those of you who skipped the first volume and are reading the second one. (Is...is that okay?) In any case, thank you for picking up this book and reading it!

Shinobi Life was originally a one-shot manga, and now it's become a real series, and here we are on volume 2! The more I think about it, the more I feel like the story is going to expand, so I'm happy that I get to draw so much!

It's all thanks to you, my readers.

When I talked to you in the first volume I was fighting a war with sleepiness, but I took all of your advice and drank coffee and stuff... Oh! By the way, now that I drink coffee to stay awake, I really like it. I used to not like it.

As I drank more and more, I seem to have figured out the way I like it (I prefer less acidic-tasting coffee). I drink a lot...which means that I'm still fighting off sleepiness. I get tired of coffee if I keep drinking it, so I drink other things too. Like Lipovitan D...stuff like that!

Oh--by the way... I usually reply when I receive letters (although sometimes it takes me a while), but sometimes I can't write back because the sender's name and address aren't on the envelope. If you ever write me a letter, please make sure you include your name and address!‽
Thank you!

Chapter 6

...WE CANNOT.

PLEASE...

YOU SHOULD NOT TOUCH ME ANYMORE.

IT'S NOT LIKE YOU'VE GOT ANYWHERE TO GO.

THERE ISN'T ANYONE ELSE WHO'D TAKE IN A WEIRD GUY LIKE YOU...

...WHO SAYS CRAZY THINGS LIKE, "I'M FROM THE PAST"...

...HITAKI.

Chapter 6/End

Chapter 7

TH...

THANKS.

NOT AT ALL.

KAGETORA IS GOING TO OBEY ORDERS.

...I KNOW HOW IT IS.

...BENI HIME-SAMA'S LIFE."

"MY MISSION IS TO PROTECT...

HE DIDN'T HESITATE TO JUMP OFF A BUILDING TO SAVE ME.

"EVEN IF MY BODY MAY PERISH...

...I SHALL PROTECT YOU."

COMPARED TO THAT...

...IT MUST BE SO MUCH EASIER FOR ME TO JUST BACK OFF.

I KNOW HE'S NOT JUST SAYING THAT.

IS SOME-THING...

...THE MATTER?

KAGETORA WILL... OBEY MY FATHER'S ORDERS.

I'M FINALLY IN THE MOST GLORIOUS OF POSITIONS!!!

NOW!

RIHITO IWATSURU-SAMA.

...WHO?

TELL ME, KAGETORA-- WHO'S THE INCREDIBLY LUCKY MAN?!!

102

FROM TIME TO TIME I SEE CORPSES LYING AT ITS EDGE...

...AND THE WIND BLOWS, BUT IT HAS NO SOUND...

...OR SCENT.

NO...IN TRUTH, IT'S MORE LIKE MY DREAM WITHIN A DREAM.

I CAN SEE NOTHING BEFORE ME.

AT THE VERY MOMENT WHEN I THINK, "I'M FINALLY DEAD"...

...SOMETHING COLD AND SOFT TOUCHES ME.

I WALK ENDLESSLY ALONG THIS ROAD, AS IT WINDS THROUGH A WITHERED GRASSLAND.

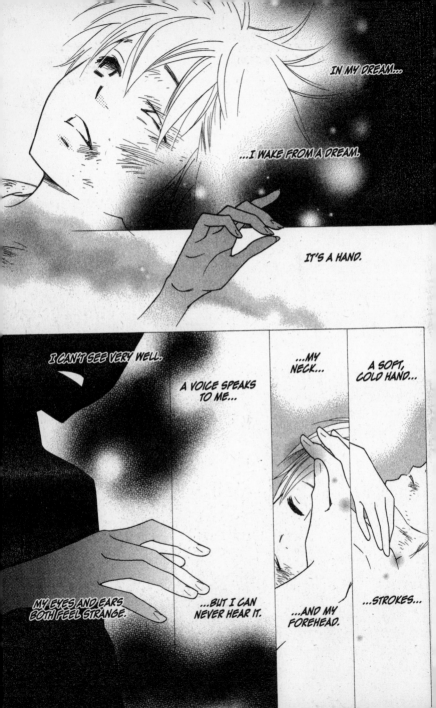

I DON'T REMEMBER...

...WHEN I FIRST HAD THIS DREAM.

ALL I KNOW IS THAT...

...IT IS THE DREAM THAT COMES WHEN...

...I SUFFER DEADLY INJURIES, AND...

...I ACHE TO REACH OUT AND GRAB...

EACH TIME I SEE THE DREAM...

...WHEN MY HEART...

...IS CLOSE TO DEATH, AS WELL.

I THOUGHT YOU LOOKED A LITTLE PALE, BUT...

...I GUESS IT WASN'T MY IMAGINATION.

I'M...FINE NOW.

...EXCUSE ME.

DON'T BE SILLY!

YOU STILL HAVE A FEVER.

109

BENI-SAMA?

WHAT ARE YOU DOING IN THE KITCHEN...?

I REALLY FEEL...

WHAT'S GOING ON?

...LIKE I WANT TO DO SOMETHING FOR HIM.

IF THERE'S ANY-THING YOU NEED, THEN--

IT'S FINE.

I WANT TO DO IT MYSELF.

KAGETORA...

HE ALWAYS DOES THINGS FOR ME.

...FOR KAGETORA.

I HAVEN'T DONE MUCH COOKING BEFORE... AND I WANT TO MAKE MEDICINE...

I'M SORRY, BUT... COULD YOU TEACH ME?

How to cook.

THEN WE'LL MAKE SOME-THING FOR HIM THAT'S EASY TO DIGEST.

Actually, it's more like... I've never cooked at all.

107

I KNOW HE'S LYING ABOUT IT BEING DELICIOUS.

ANYWAY... SO NINJAS CATCH COLDS TOO, HUH?

.....

I win!

OH!

I DIDN'T MEAN TO SOUND BIASED OR ANYTHING...

IT'S JUST--

IT'S HOT OUTSIDE, BUT...

...THE MANSION IS AS COLD AS WINTER INSIDE.

THAT BED IS FINALLY GETTING SOME USE.

OH...THE AIR CONDITIONING?

YOUR MODERN SUMMER IS DIFFERENT FROM THE SUMMER I KNOW.

...BECAUSE OF THE CHANGE IN TEMPERATURE?

DID HE...CATCH A COLD...

Maybe.

Chapter 8

122

YOU'RE BEING SO COOPERATIVE.

HMM.

ARE YOU UP TO SOMETHING?

IF I GO, I CAN MAKE A REALLY BAD IMPRESSION ON HIM.

...HAVE TO GO!

NO, NO, SOMETHING BETTER...

WHAT SHOULD I DO FIRST? KEEP HIM WAITING FOR HOURS AND NOT SHOW UP?

I'LL MAKE SURE HE DOESN'T HAVE ANY INTEREST IN MARRYING ME!!!

...I-I'LL GO.

I'LL HELP YOU GET DRESSED!

ARE YOU GOING TO THE FIRE-WORKS?

Wait, why do I even own these...?

Oh, this might be good too.

I'LL WEAR SOMETHING SO RIDICULOUS HE'LL BE HUMILIATED TO BE SEEN IN PUBLIC WITH ME!

Oh, my!

BENI-SAMA!

This?!

...SHOULD I EVEN BE SURPRISED?

WHY...

‥‥‥

IWATSURU-SAMA IS BENI-SAMA'S...

GRIND!!

EVENTUALLY THE TWO OF THEM WILL...

RIHITO IWATSURU ....!

IF SHE'S OUT LATE, I'LL BE WORRIED ABOUT HER COMING HOME ALONE. MAY I ASK YOU TO PICK HER UP?

‥‥‥

AND BEFORE YOU GO...

UM...

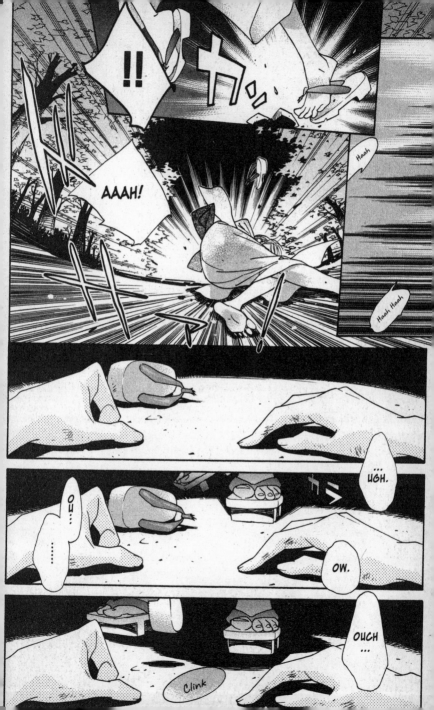

BUT I...

...SLOWLY
GETTING
WORSE.

...KEEP WATCHING
KAGETORA'S FACE...

THE PAIN IN
MY FOOT IS...

...

WHAT?

THE YU...

BUT, BENI-SAMA, YOU LOOK--

I FEEL LIKE...

I JUST WANT AS MUCH TIME WITH KAGETORA AS I CAN GET...

...AND FOR THAT, I COULD ENDURE THE PAIN IN MY FOOT FOREVER.

Chapter 8/End

...FELL.

...THAT
DIDN'T
RESIST
ME THE
WAY
WATER
SHOULD...

INTO THE
PITCH
BLACK
WATER...

I WENT DEEPER
AND DEEPER.

....I....

BENI-SAMA!!!

YOU'RE...

...BENI FUJIWARA?!

..."BENI-SAMA"...?

KAGE...

I'M NOT LETTIN' YOU OFF THAT EASY...

...SO JUST YOU SIT TIGHT.

YO.

... AGGH!

TOO BAD, YOU AIN'T IN HEAVEN YET.

I'M PRETTY NICE, HUH?

DON'T MOVE, YOU'LL OPEN YOUR WOUNDS.

...WHAT ARE YOU...

...TRYING TO SAY?

I'M SAYIN' SHE'S THE PERFECT GIRL TO SUBSTITUTE FOR THE PRINCESS.

WHEN THE GIRL YOU'RE HANKERIN' AFTER IS YOUR COUNTRY'S PRINCESS...

...THEN SHE'S WAY OUT OF *YOUR* LEAGUE.

YOU'RE JUST USIN' THAT GIRL...

...TO FILL IN FOR BENI HIME, KAGETORA.

Chapter 9/End

On purpose

THAT IS CORRECT.

LIKE, BECOMING A PART OF THE WALL AND STUFF?

"KAKUREMI-NO-JYUTSU" IS THE TECHNI-QUE WHERE YOU BLEND INTO YOUR SURROUND-INGS AND HIDE, RIGHT?

Posters everywhere!

FOR ME?!

WELL, IT WORKS FINE WHEN THE WALL'S BASICALLY BLANK, BUT...

...I THOUGHT YOU'D HAVE TROUBLE WITH THIS KIND OF WALL, SO I BOUGHT YOU SOMETHING NICE.

WHY DON'T ANY OF THESE POSTERS HAVE HEADS?

Bwa ha ha...!

Shinobi Life 2 / End

Erotically...Pitiful

Beni's everyday clothing is always too stimulating for Kagetora.

Beni
Equipment ▼
Top: Bra, parka
Bottom: Shorts

Since he realized that it's necessary to adjust to modern life...

Whoa!

...Kagetora decided to try hard, but...

FLASHING HER BARE LEGS LIKE THAT...!!!

WHAT?

But it so happened that on that day...

Awkward compliment

Mumble

Talk ▼
Warn
▶ Compliment

I...I BELIEVE THAT YOUR OUTFIT TODAY IS THE VERY BEST ONE I HAVE SEEN SO FAR...

...Beni had forgotten to wear her skirt.

Equipment ▼
Bottom: None

Ahhhh! You ninja pervert!!!

SEE YOU IN VOLUME 3!

STOP!

This is the back of the book.
You wouldn't want to spoil a great ending!

This book is printed "manga-style," in the authentic Japanese right-to-left format. Since none of the artwork has been flipped or altered, readers get to experience the story just as the creator intended. You've been asking for it, so TOKYOPOP® delivered: authentic, hot-off-the-press, and far more fun!

DIRECTIONS

If this is your first time reading manga-style, here's a quick guide to help you understand how it works.

It's easy... just start in the top right panel and follow the numbers. Have fun, and look for more 100% authentic manga from TOKYOPOP®!